HMH | (into) Math™

# Modules 12–13

Printed in the U.S.A.

ISBN 978-0-358-00216-1

2 3 4 5 6 7 8 9 10    0877    28 27 26 25 24 23 22 21 20

4500795859          B C D E F G

# Unit 4

# Addition and Subtraction in Base Ten

**Unit Opener** . . . . . 345

## MODULE 12 Understand Addition and Subtraction with Tens and Ones

Build Understanding    Connect Concepts and Skills    Apply and Practice

## MODULE 13 Two-Digit Addition and Subtraction

> Build Understanding    Connect Concepts and Skills    Apply and Practice

# Addition and Subtraction in Base Ten

Veterinarian

**STEM**
POWERING INGENUITY

Do you have a pet? How do you keep your pet healthy? Where might you take your pet if it was ill?

Veterinarians provide regular checkups to ensure that pets stay healthy. They also take care of pets when they are sick.

**STEM Task:**

Work with a partner. Look at the picture. Ask as many questions as you can.

There may be times when our friends need our help. We may notice that they look sad, frustrated, or confused. When we notice the reactions of others, we can help them to solve a problem or complete a task.

## Reflect

**Q** Look at the picture. What do you notice about the children in the picture? Describe any clues you see.

**Q** Think of a time when you helped someone else. How did you know they needed help?

# Understand Addition and Subtraction with Tens and Ones

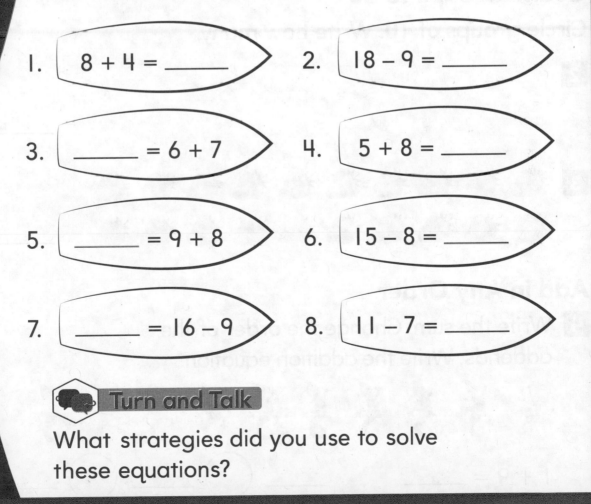

## Surfboard Search

Sammy Seal rides a surfboard that has an answer of 17.

Solve each equation. Color the surfboard that belongs to Sammy.

1. 8 + 4 = _____

2. 18 – 9 = _____

3. _____ = 6 + 7

4. 5 + 8 = _____

5. _____ = 9 + 8

6. 15 – 8 = _____

7. _____ = 16 – 9

8. 11 – 7 = _____

### Turn and Talk

What strategies did you use to solve these equations?

# Are You Ready?

Complete these problems to review prior concepts and skills you will need for this module.

## Add and Subtract

**1** Use  and to add and subtract.
Complete the equations.

$7 + 2 =$ _____

$9 - 2 =$ _____

## Count Groups to 20

Circle groups of 10. Write how many.

**2**

_____

**3**

_____

## Add in Any Order

**4** Write the sum. Change the order of the addends. Write the addition equation.

$1 + 9 =$ _____      _____ ◯ _____ ◯ _____

Name _____

# Represent Adding Tens

( I Can ) add multiples of ten with multiples of ten.

## Spark Your Learning

Start with 2 tens. Toss the number cube and add that many tens. How can you show your work?

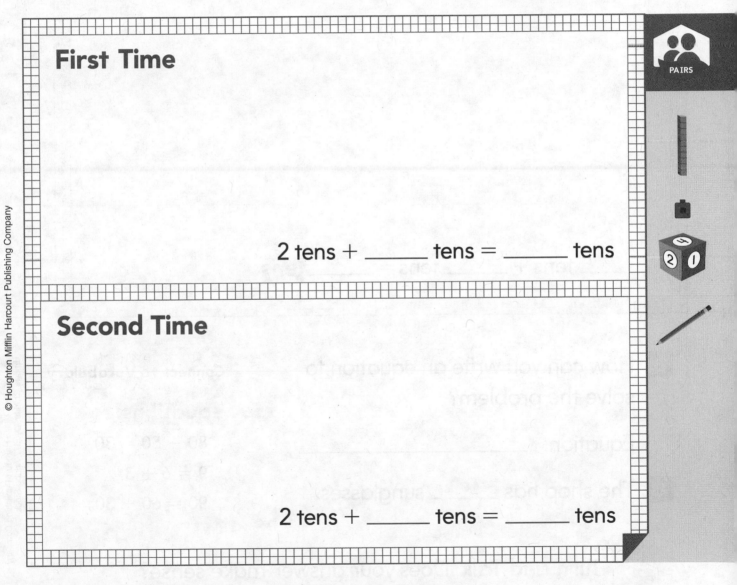

**First Time**

2 tens + _____ tens = _____ tens

**Second Time**

2 tens + _____ tens = _____ tens

Tell children they will start with 2 tens and then add some more tens. Children toss the number cube and add that many tens. Children should draw to show the addition. Have pairs repeat the activity.

Module 12 • Lesson 1

# Build Understanding

The Beach Shop has 30 adult sunglasses and 40 child sunglasses. How many sunglasses does the shop have?

**A** How can you show the problem?

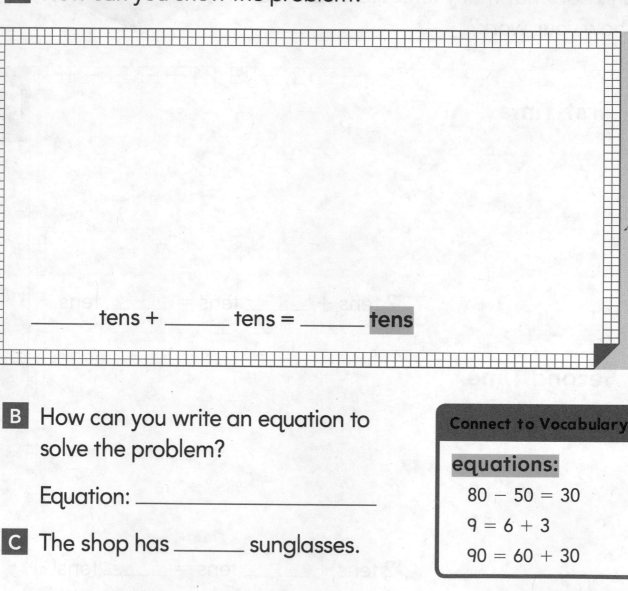

_____ tens + _____ tens = _____ **tens**

**B** How can you write an equation to solve the problem?

Equation: _____

**C** The shop has _____ sunglasses.

© Houghton Mifflin Harcourt Publishing Company • Image Credits: ©yod77/Adobe Stock

**Connect to Vocabulary**

**equations:**
80 − 50 = 30
9 = 6 + 3
90 = 60 + 30

**Turn and Talk** Does your answer make sense? How do you know?

A store has 30 large rafts and
50 small rafts. How many rafts
does the store have?

**A** Use tens to show the problem.

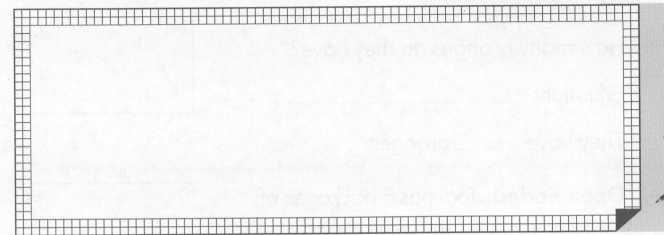

**B** Write an equation to solve the problem.

Equation: _____

**C** The store has _____ rafts.

# Check Understanding  `Math Board`

**Draw tens to show the problem.
Write an equation to solve.**

**I** Kara has 20 blue marbles. She
has 40 purple marbles. How many
marbles does Kara have?

Equation: _____

Kara has _____ marbles.

# On Your Own

Draw tens to show the problem. Write an equation to solve.

**2** (MP) **Model with Mathematics** Marcus has 20 oranges. Sally has 10 oranges. How many oranges do they have?

Equation: _____

They have _____ oranges.

---

**3** **Open Ended** Jodi has 5 packages of 10 pens each. All the pens in each package are either yellow or blue. How many of each could she have?

Equation: _____

---

**4** (MP) **Reason** Explain how to show this equation using .

$20 + 20 = 40$

_____

_____

---

⬡ **I'm in a Learning Mindset!**

What can I do to become a better learner?

_____

_____

Name _____

# Represent Subtracting Tens

( I Can ) subtract multiples of ten from multiples of ten.

## Spark Your Learning

Start with some 10-cube trains.
Hide some trains. Record below.

_____ tens started with

_____ tens left

_____ tens hidden

_____ tens started with

_____ tens left

_____ tens hidden

**PAIRS**

**Math Board**

Provide pairs with 10-cube trains (or tens blocks).
Have one partner cover his or her eyes while
the other partner hides a few of the cube trains.
How many trains are left? How many trains were
hidden? Have children write their answers, draw
to show what they did, and then switch roles.

# Build Understanding

Lori collects 40 shells at the beach.
She gives 10 shells to her sister.
How many shells does Lori have now?

**A** How can you show the problem?

_____ tens − _____ ten = _____ tens

**B** How can you write an equation to solve the problem?

Equation: _____

**C** Lori has _____ shells now.

**Turn and Talk** How does knowing the number of tens help you write an equation to solve the problem?

© Houghton Mifflin Harcourt Publishing Company • Image Credits: ©Shutterstock

There are 50 children on the beach. Some children go home. Now there are 30 children on the beach. How many children go home?

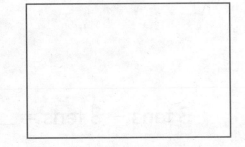

**A** Draw tens to show the problem.

**B** Write an equation for the problem.

Equation: _____

_____ children go home.

## Check Understanding

Draw tens to show the problem. Solve.

**1** There are 70 surfers in a surf contest. 40 of the surfers leave. How many surfers are left?

Equation: _____

There are _____ surfers left.

**2** _____ = 60 − 50

_____ ten = 6 tens − 5 tens

# On Your Own

**Draw tens to show your thinking.**
**Write an equation to solve.**

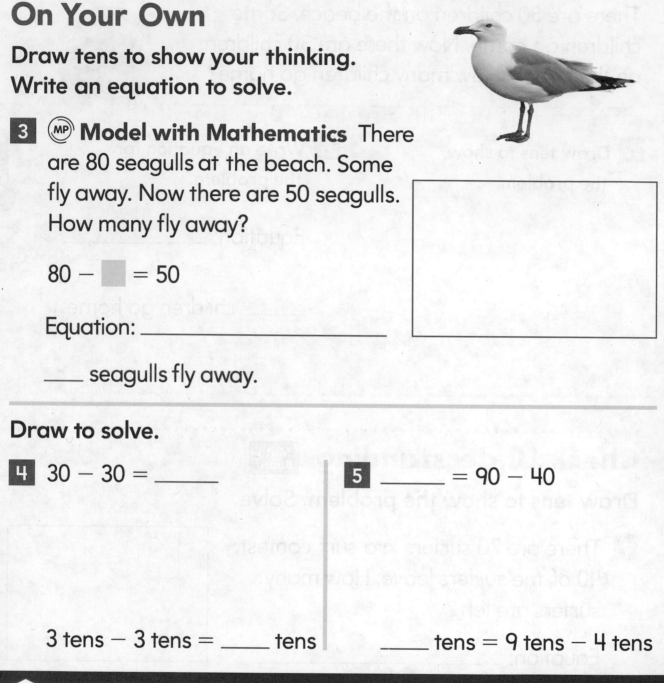

**3** (MP) **Model with Mathematics** There are 80 seagulls at the beach. Some fly away. Now there are 50 seagulls. How many fly away?

$80 - \blacksquare = 50$

Equation: _____

_____ seagulls fly away.

---

**Draw to solve.**

**4**  $30 - 30 =$ _____

**5**  _____ $= 90 - 40$

3 tens − 3 tens = _____ tens

_____ tens = 9 tens − 4 tens

---

© Houghton Mifflin Harcourt Publishing Company • Image Credits: ©Shjmyra/Adobe Stock

## ⊹ I'm in a Learning Mindset!

When I was frustrated with showing my work, how did I show my feelings appropriately?

_____

Name _____

# Add or Subtract Tens

( I Can ) add and subtract multiples of ten.

## Spark Your Learning

Use tools to add and subtract.
Record your answers on the
hundred chart.

A squirrel has _____ acorns.

Then she has _____ acorns.

Now she has _____ acorns.

| 1 | 2 | 3 | 4 | 5 | 6 | 7 | 8 | 9 | 10 |
|---|---|---|---|---|---|---|---|---|---|
| 11 | 12 | 13 | 14 | 15 | 16 | 17 | 18 | 19 | 20 |
| 21 | 22 | 23 | 24 | 25 | 26 | 27 | 28 | 29 | 30 |
| 31 | 32 | 33 | 34 | 35 | 36 | 37 | 38 | 39 | 40 |
| 41 | 42 | 43 | 44 | 45 | 46 | 47 | 48 | 49 | 50 |
| 51 | 52 | 53 | 54 | 55 | 56 | 57 | 58 | 59 | 60 |
| 61 | 62 | 63 | 64 | 65 | 66 | 67 | 68 | 69 | 70 |
| 71 | 72 | 73 | 74 | 75 | 76 | 77 | 78 | 79 | 80 |
| 81 | 82 | 83 | 84 | 85 | 86 | 87 | 88 | 89 | 90 |
| 91 | 92 | 93 | 94 | 95 | 96 | 97 | 98 | 99 | 100 |

PAIRS

Math Board

Read the following: *A squirrel has 50 acorns. She gathers 30 more acorns. Then
she buries 60 acorns. How many acorns does the squirrel have now?* Allow children
to choose tools to solve the problem, including 10-cube trains.

# Build Understanding

How can you use a hundred chart
to solve these problems?

**A** One class collects empty cans.
On Monday, they collect 30 cans.
On Tuesday, they collect 40 cans.

How many cans does the class

collect? _____ cans

| 1 | 2 | 3 | 4 | 5 | 6 | 7 | 8 | 9 | 10 |
|---|---|---|---|---|---|---|---|---|---|
| 11 | 12 | 13 | 14 | 15 | 16 | 17 | 18 | 19 | 20 |
| 21 | 22 | 23 | 24 | 25 | 26 | 27 | 28 | 29 | 30 |
| 31 | 32 | 33 | 34 | 35 | 36 | 37 | 38 | 39 | 40 |
| 41 | 42 | 43 | 44 | 45 | 46 | 47 | 48 | 49 | 50 |
| 51 | 52 | 53 | 54 | 55 | 56 | 57 | 58 | 59 | 60 |
| 61 | 62 | 63 | 64 | 65 | 66 | 67 | 68 | 69 | 70 |
| 71 | 72 | 73 | 74 | 75 | 76 | 77 | 78 | 79 | 80 |
| 81 | 82 | 83 | 84 | 85 | 86 | 87 | 88 | 89 | 90 |
| 91 | 92 | 93 | 94 | 95 | 96 | 97 | 98 | 99 | 100 |

**B** Another class wants to collect
50 bottles. The class has 20 bottles.

What does the class need to do?
Explain.

_____

_____

_____

_____

| 1 | 2 | 3 | 4 | 5 | 6 | 7 | 8 | 9 | 10 |
|---|---|---|---|---|---|---|---|---|---|
| 11 | 12 | 13 | 14 | 15 | 16 | 17 | 18 | 19 | 20 |
| 21 | 22 | 23 | 24 | 25 | 26 | 27 | 28 | 29 | 30 |
| 31 | 32 | 33 | 34 | 35 | 36 | 37 | 38 | 39 | 40 |
| 41 | 42 | 43 | 44 | 45 | 46 | 47 | 48 | 49 | 50 |
| 51 | 52 | 53 | 54 | 55 | 56 | 57 | 58 | 59 | 60 |
| 61 | 62 | 63 | 64 | 65 | 66 | 67 | 68 | 69 | 70 |
| 71 | 72 | 73 | 74 | 75 | 76 | 77 | 78 | 79 | 80 |
| 81 | 82 | 83 | 84 | 85 | 86 | 87 | 88 | 89 | 90 |
| 91 | 92 | 93 | 94 | 95 | 96 | 97 | 98 | 99 | 100 |

**Turn and Talk** Describe how to write equations
for the problems on this page.

# Step It Out

**1** Use the hundred chart to solve these problems.

**THINK:** I can move up or down rows to add and subtract tens.

| 1 | 2 | 3 | 4 | 5 | 6 | 7 | 8 | 9 | 10 |
|---|---|---|---|---|---|---|---|---|----|
| 11 | 12 | 13 | 14 | 15 | 16 | 17 | 18 | 19 | 20 |
| 21 | 22 | 23 | 24 | 25 | 26 | 27 | 28 | 29 | 30 |
| 31 | 32 | 33 | 34 | 35 | 36 | 37 | 38 | 39 | 40 |
| 41 | 42 | 43 | 44 | 45 | 46 | 47 | 48 | 49 | 50 |
| 51 | 52 | 53 | 54 | 55 | 56 | 57 | 58 | 59 | 60 |
| 61 | 62 | 63 | 64 | 65 | 66 | 67 | 68 | 69 | 70 |
| 71 | 72 | 73 | 74 | 75 | 76 | 77 | 78 | 79 | 80 |
| 81 | 82 | 83 | 84 | 85 | 86 | 87 | 88 | 89 | 90 |
| 91 | 92 | 93 | 94 | 95 | 96 | 97 | 98 | 99 | 100 |

**A** 90 − 30 = _____

**B** _____ + 20 = 30

**C** _____ = 40 + 40

**D** 30 = 80 − _____

# Check Understanding  Math Board

Solve. Write an equation to show the problem.

**1** There are 20 fish in a tank. 50 more fish are put in the tank. How many fish are in the tank now?

| 1 | 2 | 3 | 4 | 5 | 6 | 7 | 8 | 9 | 10 |
|---|---|---|---|---|---|---|---|---|----|
| 11 | 12 | 13 | 14 | 15 | 16 | 17 | 18 | 19 | 20 |
| 21 | 22 | 23 | 24 | 25 | 26 | 27 | 28 | 29 | 30 |
| 31 | 32 | 33 | 34 | 35 | 36 | 37 | 38 | 39 | 40 |
| 41 | 42 | 43 | 44 | 45 | 46 | 47 | 48 | 49 | 50 |
| 51 | 52 | 53 | 54 | 55 | 56 | 57 | 58 | 59 | 60 |
| 61 | 62 | 63 | 64 | 65 | 66 | 67 | 68 | 69 | 70 |
| 71 | 72 | 73 | 74 | 75 | 76 | 77 | 78 | 79 | 80 |
| 81 | 82 | 83 | 84 | 85 | 86 | 87 | 88 | 89 | 90 |
| 91 | 92 | 93 | 94 | 95 | 96 | 97 | 98 | 99 | 100 |

Equation: _____

_____ fish

**Add or subtract.**

**2** 50 + _____ = 80

**3** _____ = 90 − 20

# On Your Own

**(MP) Model with Mathematics** Write an addition or subtraction equation to solve.

**4** Dan has 20 jars. He finds more jars. Now he has 60 jars. How many jars does Dan find?

Equation: _____

_____ jars

**5** Rachel has 60 cups. Nate gives her 10 cups. How many cups does Rachel have now?

Equation: _____

_____ cups

**6** Seeds form in flowers. Seeds grow into new plants. Trisha has 70 flower seeds. She plants 30 seeds. How many seeds does she still need to plant?

Equation: _____

_____ seeds

## I'm in a Learning Mindset!

How am I managing my learning with adding and subtracting tens?

_____

_____

Keep Going **to** Practice and Homework Journal

Name _____

# Use a Hundred Chart to Add

**I Can** use a hundred chart to add two-digit numbers with one-digit numbers or multiples of ten.

## Spark Your Learning

Meg has some toy rings. She gets 20 more rings. Now she has 50 rings. How can you find how many rings Meg starts with?

Meg starts with _____ rings.

Read the problem above aloud. Have children choose tools and solve the problem.

# Build Understanding

How can you use a hundred chart to solve these problems?

**A** There are 5 blue hats and 22 red hats. How many hats are there altogether?

Equation: _____

_____ hats

| 1 | 2 | 3 | 4 | 5 | 6 | 7 | 8 | 9 | 10 |
|---|---|---|---|---|---|---|---|---|---|
| 11 | 12 | 13 | 14 | 15 | 16 | 17 | 18 | 19 | 20 |
| 21 | 22 | 23 | 24 | 25 | 26 | 27 | 28 | 29 | 30 |
| 31 | 32 | 33 | 34 | 35 | 36 | 37 | 38 | 39 | 40 |
| 41 | 42 | 43 | 44 | 45 | 46 | 47 | 48 | 49 | 50 |
| 51 | 52 | 53 | 54 | 55 | 56 | 57 | 58 | 59 | 60 |
| 61 | 62 | 63 | 64 | 65 | 66 | 67 | 68 | 69 | 70 |
| 71 | 72 | 73 | 74 | 75 | 76 | 77 | 78 | 79 | 80 |
| 81 | 82 | 83 | 84 | 85 | 86 | 87 | 88 | 89 | 90 |
| 91 | 92 | 93 | 94 | 95 | 96 | 97 | 98 | 99 | 100 |

**B** Carol sees 16 red hats and 6 yellow hats in a store. How many red and yellow hats does she see?

_____ hats

Explain how you counted on by **ones**.

_____

_____

_____

| 1 | 2 | 3 | 4 | 5 | 6 | 7 | 8 | 9 | 10 |
|---|---|---|---|---|---|---|---|---|---|
| 11 | 12 | 13 | 14 | 15 | 16 | 17 | 18 | 19 | 20 |
| 21 | 22 | 23 | 24 | 25 | 26 | 27 | 28 | 29 | 30 |
| 31 | 32 | 33 | 34 | 35 | 36 | 37 | 38 | 39 | 40 |
| 41 | 42 | 43 | 44 | 45 | 46 | 47 | 48 | 49 | 50 |
| 51 | 52 | 53 | 54 | 55 | 56 | 57 | 58 | 59 | 60 |
| 61 | 62 | 63 | 64 | 65 | 66 | 67 | 68 | 69 | 70 |
| 71 | 72 | 73 | 74 | 75 | 76 | 77 | 78 | 79 | 80 |
| 81 | 82 | 83 | 84 | 85 | 86 | 87 | 88 | 89 | 90 |
| 91 | 92 | 93 | 94 | 95 | 96 | 97 | 98 | 99 | 100 |

**Turn and Talk** How can you use the hundred chart to add 16 + 60?

# Step It Out

Use a hundred chart to add tens to a number.

| 1 | 2 | 3 | 4 | 5 | 6 | 7 | 8 | 9 | 10 |
|---|---|---|---|---|---|---|---|---|---|
| 11 | 12 | 13 | 14 | 15 | 16 | 17 | 18 | 19 | 20 |
| 21 | 22 | 23 | 24 | 25 | 26 | 27 | 28 | 29 | 30 |
| 31 | 32 | 33 | 34 | 35 | 36 | 37 | 38 | 39 | 40 |
| 41 | 42 | 43 | 44 | 45 | 46 | 47 | 48 | 49 | 50 |
| 51 | 52 | 53 | 54 | 55 | 56 | 57 | 58 | 59 | 60 |
| 61 | 62 | 63 | 64 | 65 | 66 | 67 | 68 | 69 | 70 |
| 71 | 72 | 73 | 74 | 75 | 76 | 77 | 78 | 79 | 80 |
| 81 | 82 | 83 | 84 | 85 | 86 | 87 | 88 | 89 | 90 |
| 91 | 92 | 93 | 94 | 95 | 96 | 97 | 98 | 99 | 100 |

**1** Solve $40 + 28 =$ ▢.

**A** Circle the number 28.

**B** Add 4 tens.

**THINK:** Count by tens. Move down 4 rows.

**C** Write the sum.

$40 + 28 =$ _____

Use the hundred chart to solve.

**2** $62 + 30 =$ _____  |  **3** _____ $= 35 + 20$

# Check Understanding  [Math Board]

Use the hundred chart to solve.

**1** Sarah has 5 crayons. Marc has 24 crayons. How many crayons do they have together?

Equation: _____

_____ crayons

| 1 | 2 | 3 | 4 | 5 | 6 | 7 | 8 | 9 | 10 |
|---|---|---|---|---|---|---|---|---|---|
| 11 | 12 | 13 | 14 | 15 | 16 | 17 | 18 | 19 | 20 |
| 21 | 22 | 23 | 24 | 25 | 26 | 27 | 28 | 29 | 30 |
| 31 | 32 | 33 | 34 | 35 | 36 | 37 | 38 | 39 | 40 |
| 41 | 42 | 43 | 44 | 45 | 46 | 47 | 48 | 49 | 50 |
| 51 | 52 | 53 | 54 | 55 | 56 | 57 | 58 | 59 | 60 |
| 61 | 62 | 63 | 64 | 65 | 66 | 67 | 68 | 69 | 70 |
| 71 | 72 | 73 | 74 | 75 | 76 | 77 | 78 | 79 | 80 |
| 81 | 82 | 83 | 84 | 85 | 86 | 87 | 88 | 89 | 90 |
| 91 | 92 | 93 | 94 | 95 | 96 | 97 | 98 | 99 | 100 |

# On Your Own

**Use the hundred chart to solve.**

| 1 | 2 | 3 | 4 | 5 | 6 | 7 | 8 | 9 | 10 |
|---|---|---|---|---|---|---|---|---|---|
| 11 | 12 | 13 | 14 | 15 | 16 | 17 | 18 | 19 | 20 |
| 21 | 22 | 23 | 24 | 25 | 26 | 27 | 28 | 29 | 30 |
| 31 | 32 | 33 | 34 | 35 | 36 | 37 | 38 | 39 | 40 |
| 41 | 42 | 43 | 44 | 45 | 46 | 47 | 48 | 49 | 50 |
| 51 | 52 | 53 | 54 | 55 | 56 | 57 | 58 | 59 | 60 |
| 61 | 62 | 63 | 64 | 65 | 66 | 67 | 68 | 69 | 70 |
| 71 | 72 | 73 | 74 | 75 | 76 | 77 | 78 | 79 | 80 |
| 81 | 82 | 83 | 84 | 85 | 86 | 87 | 88 | 89 | 90 |
| 91 | 92 | 93 | 94 | 95 | 96 | 97 | 98 | 99 | 100 |

**2** (MP) **Use Tools** Chris counts 12 cars, and then he counts 6 more. How many cars does he count? Write the equation.

Equation: _____

Chris counts _____ cars.

**3** **Open Ended** Evie adds tens to a number and gets a sum of 57. What two numbers could she add?

Numbers: _____ and _____

**Solve.**

**4** $20 + 55 =$ _____

**5** _____ $= 22 + 4$

## 🔲 I'm in a Learning Mindset!

How did members of my group approach problem 3 differently?

_____

Name _____

# Represent Addition with Tens and Ones

( I Can ) show how to add a one-digit number or a multiple of ten to a two-digit number by combining tens and ones.

## Spark Your Learning

Jen has 23 toy boats. She gets 5 more toy boats. How many toy boats does she have?

How can you solve this problem?

**PAIRS**

**Math Board**

Jen has _____ toy boats.

Read the problem aloud. Have children work together to solve the problem. Have children draw to show their work.

# Build Understanding

Ms. Gray has 12 paintbrushes.
She gets 5 more paintbrushes. How
many paintbrushes does she have?

**A** Draw to show how to add the ones.

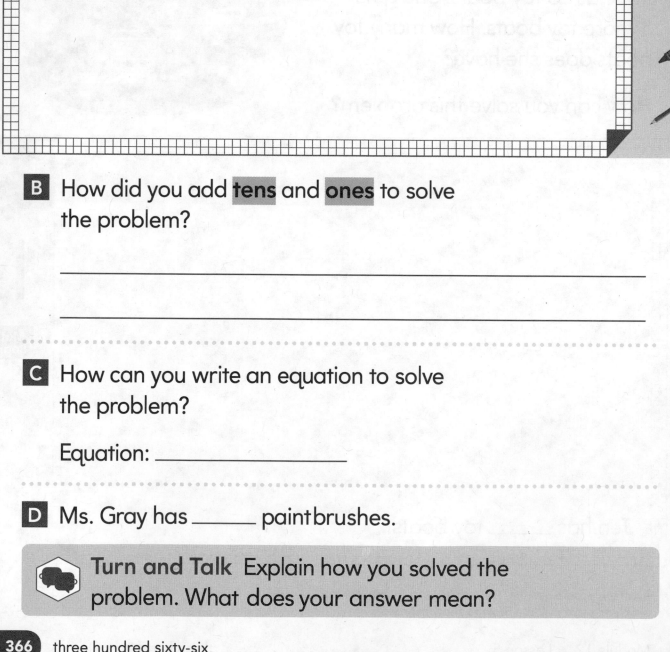

**B** How did you add **tens** and **ones** to solve
the problem?

_____

_____

**C** How can you write an equation to solve
the problem?

Equation: _____

**D** Ms. Gray has _____ paintbrushes.

**Turn and Talk** Explain how you solved the
problem. What does your answer mean?

# Step It Out

**I** There are 20 paint jars in a store.
The store gets 34 more paint jars.
How many paint jars does the store have?

**A** Draw to show the problem. Start with 20.

**THINK:** I can draw a group of 2 tens.

**B** Draw to show the number of paint
jars the store gets.

**THINK:** I can draw another group
of 3 tens 4 ones.

**C** Show how to add the tens.

**THINK:** I can draw a circle to group
the tens.

**D** Solve the problem.

Equation: _____ _____ paint jars

# Check Understanding  Math Board

**Use tens and ones to add. Show your work.**

**I** Julia has 3 crayons. Rich gives her
24 more crayons. How many
crayons does Julia have?

Equation: _____

Julia has _____ crayons.

# On Your Own

(MP) **Model with Mathematics** Use tens and ones to add. Show your work.

**Plant Sale**

**2** Ms. Gia has 55 plants. She gets 3 more plants. How many plants does she have now?

Equation: _____

Ms. Gia has _____ plants.

**3** There are 42 red flowers. There are 20 yellow flowers. How many flowers are there?

Equation: _____

There are _____ flowers.

**Solve the equations.**

**4** $5 + 21 =$ _____

**5** _____ $= 40 + 5$

**6** _____ $= 71 + 1$

**7** _____ $= 62 + 6$

**8** $55 + 20 =$ _____

**9** $38 + 40 =$ _____

## I'm in a Learning Mindset!

How did I show patience when I was writing equations to solve problems?

_____

Keep Going ▶ Practice and Homework Journal

© Houghton Mifflin Harcourt Publishing Company

Name _____

# Represent Make Ten to Add

( I Can ) use the *make a ten* strategy to add a two-digit number and a one-digit number.

## Spark Your Learning

Ryan has 39 lemons. Toss the number cube to find out how many more lemons he gets. How many lemons does Ryan have now?

How can you show the problem?

Ryan gets _____ more lemons.

Ryan has _____ lemons now.

Read the problem to children. Have each group of children toss the number cube and write the number they tossed. Next, have children choose tools to show the problem and solve the problem.

# Build Understanding

There are 47 books on a shelf. There are 9 books on another shelf. How many books are on the two shelves?

**A** How can you make a ten to solve the problem?

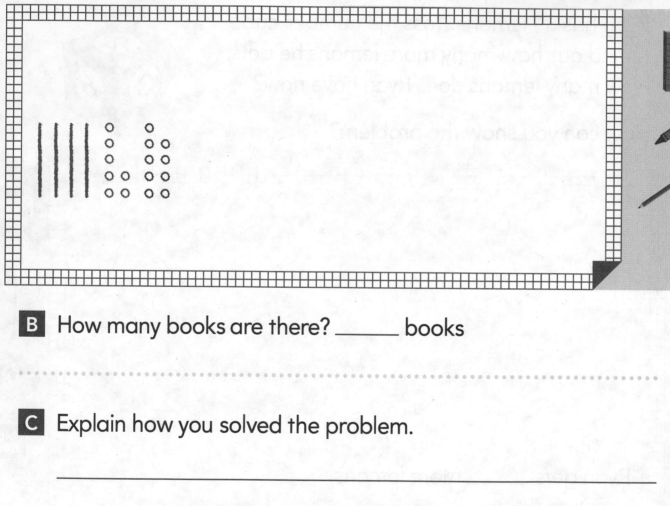

**B** How many books are there? _____ books

**C** Explain how you solved the problem.

_____

_____

_____

**Turn and Talk** How does making a ten help you solve the problem?

# Step It Out

**I** ▶ There are 26 red butterflies and 8 blue butterflies. How many butterflies are there?

Make a ten to solve this problem.

**A** First, show the 26 red butterflies.

_____ tens _____ ones

**B** Then, show the blue butterflies.

**THINK:** Show a group of _____ ones.

**C** Group 6 ones and 4 ones to make a ten.

Now, there are _____ tens _____ ones.

**D** Write an equation to solve the problem.

Equation: _____

**E** There are _____ red and blue butterflies.

**Turn and Talk** What other equation could you write to solve this problem?

# Step It Out

**2** 17 children are in the pool. 6 more children join them. How many children are in the pool?

Make a ten to solve the problem.

**A** First, draw to show the numbers 17 and 6.

**B** Group 7 ones and 3 ones to make a ten.

Now, there are _____ tens _____ ones.

**C** Write an equation to solve the problem.

Equation: _____

**D** _____ children are in the pool.

......................................................

# Check Understanding  [Math Board]

Make a ten to solve.

**1** Jay has 16 pens. Ella has 9 pens. How many pens do they have altogether?

Equation: _____

Jay and Ella have _____ pens.

# On Your Own

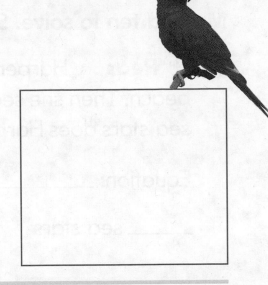

**MP** **Use Structure** Make a ten to solve.
Show your work.

**2** Karen counts 46 birds.
Then she counts 7 more birds.
How many birds does she count?

Equation: _____

_____ birds

**3** Pat has 44 oranges and 9 grapefruits
in a box. How many oranges and
grapefruits does he have in the box?

Equation: _____

_____ oranges and grapefruits

## Make a ten to solve.

| | | |
|---|---|---|
| **4** | **5** | **6** |
| $3 + 29 = $ _____ | _____ $ = 42 + 9$ | _____ $ = 67 + 7$ |
| **7** | **8** | **9** |
| $9 + 17 = $ _____ | _____ $ = 58 + 6$ | $37 + 8 = $ _____ |

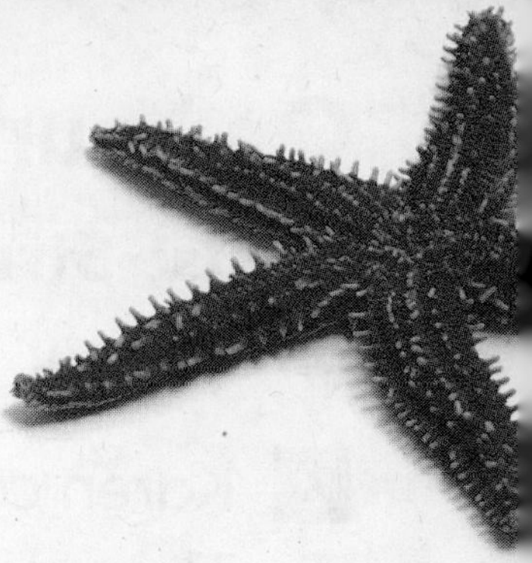

## On Your Own

**Make a ten to solve. Show your work.**

**10** (MP) **Reason** Harper sees 16 sea stars on the beach. Then she sees 8 more. How many sea stars does Harper see?

Equation: ____________________

______ sea stars

**11** Pia has 56 markers. Mary has 9 markers. How many markers do Pia and Mary have?

______ markers

**Open Ended** How did you make a ten to find the sum? Explain.

______________________________________________

______________________________________________



### I'm in a Learning Mindset!

What strategy do I like to use the most? Why?

______________________________________________

______________________________________________



Keep Going to Practice and Homework Journal

Name _____

# Represent Make Ten to Add with a Visual Model

**I Can** use a visual model to show how to use the *make a ten* strategy to add a two-digit number and a one-digit number.

## Spark Your Learning

Ava has 48 stickers. Logan gives her 4 stickers. How many stickers does Ava have now?

How can you show this problem?

Ava has _____ stickers.

Read the problem aloud. Have children choose tools to solve the problem.

PAIRS

Math Board

© Houghton Mifflin Harcourt Publishing Company

# Build Understanding

8 puppies are in the park. 6 puppies join them. How many puppies are in the park now?

How can you use a number line to show how to make a ten?

**A** If you start at 8, how many would you jump

to get to 10? _____

Draw to show your thinking.

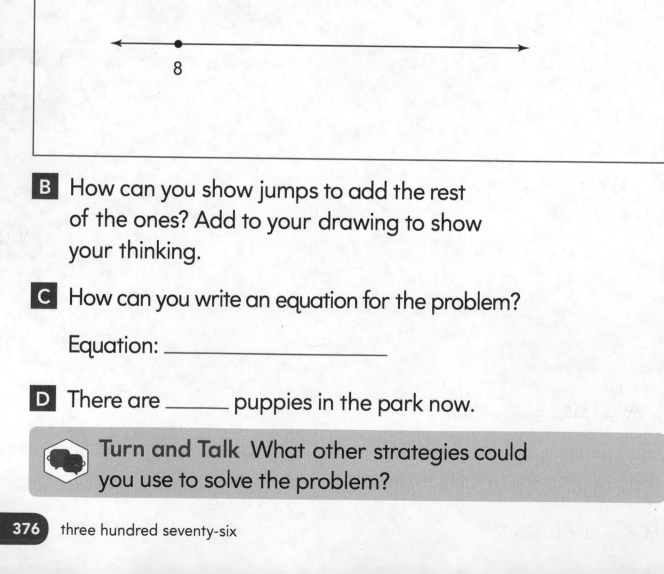

**B** How can you show jumps to add the rest of the ones? Add to your drawing to show your thinking.

**C** How can you write an equation for the problem?

Equation: _____

**D** There are _____ puppies in the park now.

**Turn and Talk** What other strategies could you use to solve the problem?

## Step It Out

**I** Mr. Lind sells 57 fruit pops at the fair.
Then he sells 9 more. How many
fruit pops does Mr. Lind sell?

Make a ten to solve this problem.

**A** Start at 57 on the number line.
First, jump 3 to make a ten. Then add the rest.
Write the numbers.

**THINK:** I need to add 9 altogether.

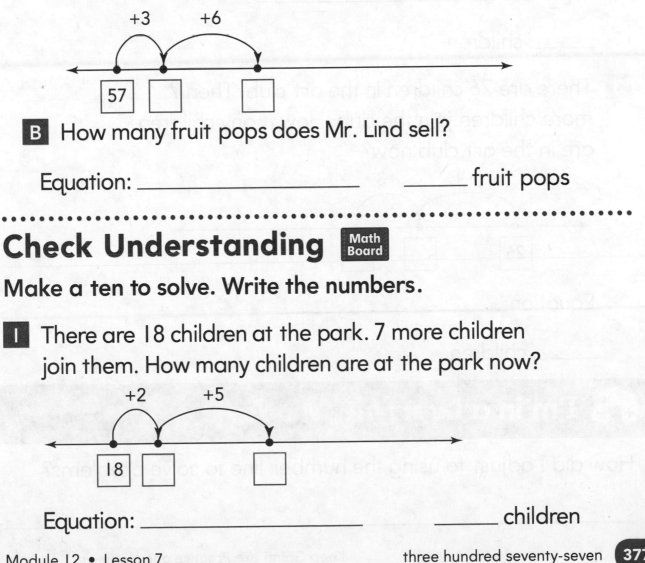

+3     +6

[ 57 ]  [  ]     [  ]

**B** How many fruit pops does Mr. Lind sell?

Equation: _____     _____ fruit pops

## Check Understanding  [Math Board]

**Make a ten to solve. Write the numbers.**

**I** There are 18 children at the park. 7 more children
join them. How many children are at the park now?

+2     +5

[ 18 ]  [  ]     [  ]

Equation: _____     _____ children

© Houghton Mifflin Harcourt Publishing Company

# On Your Own

(MP) **Use Repeated Reasoning** Make a ten to solve.

**2** There are 19 children in the computer club. 6 more join the club. How many children are in the computer club now?

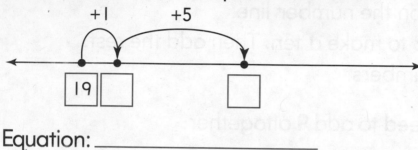

Equation: _____

_____ children

**3** There are 26 children in the art club. Then 7 more children join the club. How many children are in the art club now?

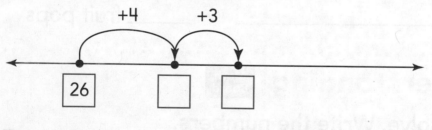

Equation: _____

_____ children

---

## I'm in a Learning Mindset!

How did I adjust to using the number line to solve problems?

_____

Name _____

# Use Mental Math to Find 10 Less and 10 More

( I Can ) show 10 less or 10 more than a number without having to count.

## Step It Out

**1** March had 10 fewer rainy days than April. May had 10 more rainy days than April. April had 13 rainy days. How many rainy days were there in March and May?

**A** April had 13 rainy days.

THINK: 13 is _____ ten _____ ones.

**B** March had 10 less than April.

THINK: Take _____ ten away from 13.

**C** May had 10 more than April.

THINK: Add _____ ten to 13.

**D** Write the numbers.

|  | 13 |  |
|---|---|---|
| _____ | April | _____ |
| **March** |  | **May** |
| 10 less than 13 |  | 10 more than 13 |

# Step It Out

**2** What numbers are 10 less and 10 more than 44?

**A** Circle the number 44 on the hundred chart.

| 1 | 2 | 3 | 4 | 5 | 6 | 7 | 8 | 9 | 10 |
|---|---|---|---|---|---|---|---|---|---|
| 11 | 12 | 13 | 14 | 15 | 16 | 17 | 18 | 19 | 20 |
| 21 | 22 | 23 | 24 | 25 | 26 | 27 | 28 | 29 | 30 |
| 31 | 32 | 33 | 34 | 35 | 36 | 37 | 38 | 39 | 40 |
| 41 | 42 | 43 | 44 | 45 | 46 | 47 | 48 | 49 | 50 |
| 51 | 52 | 53 | 54 | 55 | 56 | 57 | 58 | 59 | 60 |
| 61 | 62 | 63 | 64 | 65 | 66 | 67 | 68 | 69 | 70 |
| 71 | 72 | 73 | 74 | 75 | 76 | 77 | 78 | 79 | 80 |
| 81 | 82 | 83 | 84 | 85 | 86 | 87 | 88 | 89 | 90 |
| 91 | 92 | 93 | 94 | 95 | 96 | 97 | 98 | 99 | 100 |

**B** What number is 10 less than 44? Circle the number.

**THINK:** Move up one row from 44.

**C** What number is 10 more than 44? Circle the number.

**THINK:** Move down one row from 44.

**D** Write the numbers to solve.

_____          44          _____

10 less than 44          10 more than 44

**Turn and Talk** Explain why the tens digit increases or decreases by 1 when 10 is added or subtracted from a number.

# Check Understanding  Math Board

Write the numbers that are 10 less and 10 more.

**1**

_____ 25 _____

**2**

_____ 67 _____

## On Your Own

**3** (MP) **Reason** Susan, Tracy, and Kris each
have a rock collection. Susan has 48 rocks in
her collection. Tracy has 10 more rocks than
Susan. Kris has 10 more rocks than Tracy.
How many rocks do Tracy and Kris
each have?

**A** Write the number of rocks Tracy and
Kris have.

Tracy has _____ rocks.

Kris has _____ rocks.

**B** How many fewer rocks does Tracy have
than Kris? Explain your reasoning.

_____

_____

_____

**Write the numbers that are 10 less and 10 more.**

**4**

_____ 26 _____

**5**

_____ 30 _____

**6**

_____ 74 _____

**7**

_____ 83 _____

# On Your Own

**8** (MP) **Attend to Precision** Draw lines to match the card to the number.

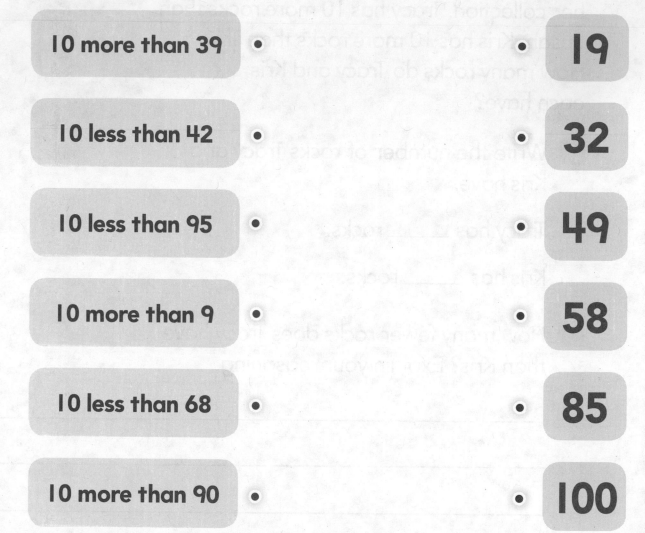

| | |
|---|---|
| 10 more than 39 • | • **19** |
| 10 less than 42 • | • **32** |
| 10 less than 95 • | • **49** |
| 10 more than 9 • | • **58** |
| 10 less than 68 • | • **85** |
| 10 more than 90 • | • **100** |

## Write the numbers that are 10 less and 10 more.

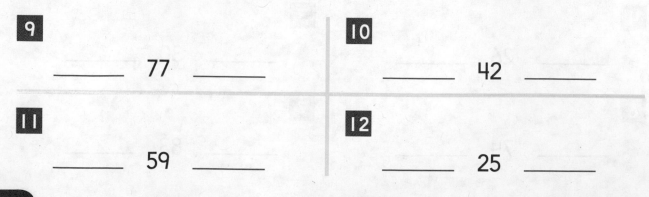

**9**
_____ 77 _____

**10**
_____ 42 _____

**11**
_____ 59 _____

**12**
_____ 25 _____

Keep Going ▶ Practice and Homework Journal

Name _____

# 12 Review

## Vocabulary

1 What is an equation? Show an example.

_____

## Concepts and Skills

**Use the hundred chart to solve.**

| 1 | 2 | 3 | 4 | 5 | 6 | 7 | 8 | 9 | 10 |
|---|---|---|---|---|---|---|---|---|---|
| 11 | 12 | 13 | 14 | 15 | 16 | 17 | 18 | 19 | 20 |
| 21 | 22 | 23 | 24 | 25 | 26 | 27 | 28 | 29 | 30 |
| 31 | 32 | 33 | 34 | 35 | 36 | 37 | 38 | 39 | 40 |
| 41 | 42 | 43 | 44 | 45 | 46 | 47 | 48 | 49 | 50 |
| 51 | 52 | 53 | 54 | 55 | 56 | 57 | 58 | 59 | 60 |
| 61 | 62 | 63 | 64 | 65 | 66 | 67 | 68 | 69 | 70 |
| 71 | 72 | 73 | 74 | 75 | 76 | 77 | 78 | 79 | 80 |
| 81 | 82 | 83 | 84 | 85 | 86 | 87 | 88 | 89 | 90 |
| 91 | 92 | 93 | 94 | 95 | 96 | 97 | 98 | 99 | 100 |

2 Carlos has 15 toy trains. Marcel has 9 toy trains. How many toy trains do they have altogether?

Equation: _____

_____ toy trains

**Make a ten to solve. Show your work.**

3 There are 18 children at the beach. Then 5 more children come to the beach. How many children are at the beach now?

Equation: _____

_____ children

**Write the numbers that are 10 less and 10 more.**

4 _____ 75 _____

5 _____ 12 _____

**Draw tens to show the problem.**
**Write an equation to solve.**

**6** Fran has 50 marbles. She gives Caitlyn 20 marbles. How many marbles does Fran have now?

Equation: _____

Fran has _____ marbles.

---

**Fill in the bubble next to the correct answer.**

**7** What is 31 + 5?

○ 33     ○ 36     ○ 39

**8** What is 20 + 40?

○ 20     ○ 60     ○ 70

---

**Write an equation to solve.**

**9** There are 20 green apples and 30 red apples. How many apples are there?

Equation: _____     _____ apples

---

**Make a ten to solve. Write the numbers.**

**10** There are 16 flavors of fruit pops. 9 more flavors are added. How many flavors are there now?

Equation: _____     _____ flavors

# Two-Digit Addition and Subtraction

## Puzzle Piece ADDITION

Write addends to complete each puzzle.

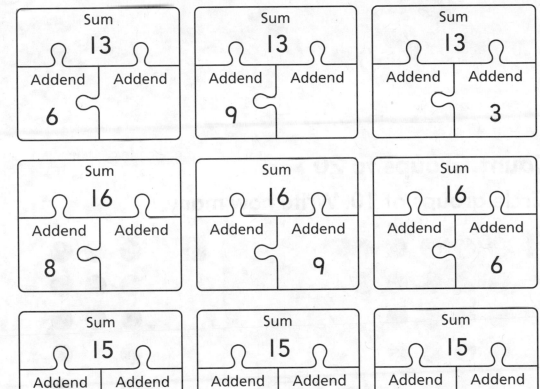

| Sum 13 | Sum 13 | Sum 13 |
| Addend 6 / Addend | Addend 9 / Addend | Addend / Addend 3 |

| Sum 16 | Sum 16 | Sum 16 |
| Addend 8 / Addend | Addend / Addend 9 | Addend / Addend 6 |

| Sum 15 | Sum 15 | Sum 15 |
| Addend / Addend | Addend / Addend | Addend / Addend 5 |

💬 Turn and Talk

How could you write three different ways to make a sum of 20?

# Are You Ready?

Complete these problems to review prior concepts and skills you will need for this module.

## Add Groups

Circle the two groups to put them together. Complete the addition equation.

**1**

_____ + _____ = _____

## Count Groups to 20

Circle groups of 10. Write how many.

**2**

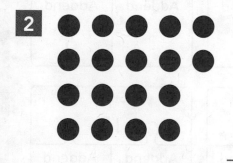

**3**

_____

_____

## Tens

Write the number.

**4**

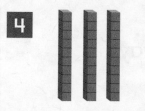

_____

**5**

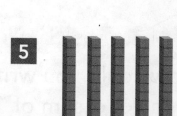

_____

Name _____

# Use a Hundred Chart to Show Two-Digit Addition and Subtraction

( I Can ) use a hundred chart to add or subtract two-digit numbers.

## Spark Your Learning

Use tools to add and subtract. Record your answers.

There are _____ birds.

Then _____ more birds come.

Now there are _____ birds in the tree.

| 1 | 2 | 3 | 4 | 5 | 6 | 7 | 8 | 9 | 10 |
|---|---|---|---|---|---|---|---|---|---|
| 11 | 12 | 13 | 14 | 15 | 16 | 17 | 18 | 19 | 20 |
| 21 | 22 | 23 | 24 | 25 | 26 | 27 | 28 | 29 | 30 |
| 31 | 32 | 33 | 34 | 35 | 36 | 37 | 38 | 39 | 40 |
| 41 | 42 | 43 | 44 | 45 | 46 | 47 | 48 | 49 | 50 |
| 51 | 52 | 53 | 54 | 55 | 56 | 57 | 58 | 59 | 60 |
| 61 | 62 | 63 | 64 | 65 | 66 | 67 | 68 | 69 | 70 |
| 71 | 72 | 73 | 74 | 75 | 76 | 77 | 78 | 79 | 80 |
| 81 | 82 | 83 | 84 | 85 | 86 | 87 | 88 | 89 | 90 |
| 91 | 92 | 93 | 94 | 95 | 96 | 97 | 98 | 99 | 100 |

PAIRS

Math Board

Read the following aloud: *There are 36 birds in a tree. More birds come. Now there are 56 birds in the tree. How many birds come to the tree?* Have children choose tools to solve the problem.

# Build Understanding

How can you use the hundred chart to solve these problems?

**A** There are 30 frogs in a pond. Some frogs hop away. There are 10 frogs left. How many frogs hop away?

_____ frogs

| 1 | 2 | 3 | 4 | 5 | 6 | 7 | 8 | 9 | 10 |
|---|---|---|---|---|---|---|---|---|---|
| 11 | 12 | 13 | 14 | 15 | 16 | 17 | 18 | 19 | 20 |
| 21 | 22 | 23 | 24 | 25 | 26 | 27 | 28 | 29 | 30 |
| 31 | 32 | 33 | 34 | 35 | 36 | 37 | 38 | 39 | 40 |
| 41 | 42 | 43 | 44 | 45 | 46 | 47 | 48 | 49 | 50 |
| 51 | 52 | 53 | 54 | 55 | 56 | 57 | 58 | 59 | 60 |
| 61 | 62 | 63 | 64 | 65 | 66 | 67 | 68 | 69 | 70 |
| 71 | 72 | 73 | 74 | 75 | 76 | 77 | 78 | 79 | 80 |
| 81 | 82 | 83 | 84 | 85 | 86 | 87 | 88 | 89 | 90 |
| 91 | 92 | 93 | 94 | 95 | 96 | 97 | 98 | 99 | 100 |

**B** Haley sees 38 sheep in the barn. She sees more sheep in the field. She sees 78 sheep in all. How many sheep does she see in the field?

_____ sheep

• How did you use the hundred chart to solve the problem? Explain.

| 1 | 2 | 3 | 4 | 5 | 6 | 7 | 8 | 9 | 10 |
|---|---|---|---|---|---|---|---|---|---|
| 11 | 12 | 13 | 14 | 15 | 16 | 17 | 18 | 19 | 20 |
| 21 | 22 | 23 | 24 | 25 | 26 | 27 | 28 | 29 | 30 |
| 31 | 32 | 33 | 34 | 35 | 36 | 37 | 38 | 39 | 40 |
| 41 | 42 | 43 | 44 | 45 | 46 | 47 | 48 | 49 | 50 |
| 51 | 52 | 53 | 54 | 55 | 56 | 57 | 58 | 59 | 60 |
| 61 | 62 | 63 | 64 | 65 | 66 | 67 | 68 | 69 | 70 |
| 71 | 72 | 73 | 74 | 75 | 76 | 77 | 78 | 79 | 80 |
| 81 | 82 | 83 | 84 | 85 | 86 | 87 | 88 | 89 | 90 |
| 91 | 92 | 93 | 94 | 95 | 96 | 97 | 98 | 99 | 100 |

_____

_____

 **Turn and Talk** How can you use the hundred chart to subtract?

© Houghton Mifflin Harcourt Publishing Company

# Step It Out

**1** There are 45 trees in a park. More trees are planted. Now there are 65 trees. How many trees are planted?

$45 +$ ⬜ $= 65$

| 1 | 2 | 3 | 4 | 5 | 6 | 7 | 8 | 9 | 10 |
|---|---|---|---|---|---|---|---|---|---|
| 11 | 12 | 13 | 14 | 15 | 16 | 17 | 18 | 19 | 20 |
| 21 | 22 | 23 | 24 | 25 | 26 | 27 | 28 | 29 | 30 |
| 31 | 32 | 33 | 34 | 35 | 36 | 37 | 38 | 39 | 40 |
| 41 | 42 | 43 | 44 | 45 | 46 | 47 | 48 | 49 | 50 |
| 51 | 52 | 53 | 54 | 55 | 56 | 57 | 58 | 59 | 60 |
| 61 | 62 | 63 | 64 | 65 | 66 | 67 | 68 | 69 | 70 |
| 71 | 72 | 73 | 74 | 75 | 76 | 77 | 78 | 79 | 80 |
| 81 | 82 | 83 | 84 | 85 | 86 | 87 | 88 | 89 | 90 |
| 91 | 92 | 93 | 94 | 95 | 96 | 97 | 98 | 99 | 100 |

**A** Start at the number 45.

**B** Use the hundred chart to add.

**THINK:** I can **count on** tens to get to 65.

Count on _____ tens.

_____ tens = _____

**C** _____ more trees were planted.

· · · · · · · · · · · · · · · · · · · · · · · · · · · · · · · · · · · · · · · · · · · · · · · · ·

# Check Understanding  Math Board

Use the hundred chart to solve.

**1** There are 80 bees in a hive. Some bees fly away. There are 50 bees left. How many bees fly away?

_____ bees

| 1 | 2 | 3 | 4 | 5 | 6 | 7 | 8 | 9 | 10 |
|---|---|---|---|---|---|---|---|---|---|
| 11 | 12 | 13 | 14 | 15 | 16 | 17 | 18 | 19 | 20 |
| 21 | 22 | 23 | 24 | 25 | 26 | 27 | 28 | 29 | 30 |
| 31 | 32 | 33 | 34 | 35 | 36 | 37 | 38 | 39 | 40 |
| 41 | 42 | 43 | 44 | 45 | 46 | 47 | 48 | 49 | 50 |
| 51 | 52 | 53 | 54 | 55 | 56 | 57 | 58 | 59 | 60 |
| 61 | 62 | 63 | 64 | 65 | 66 | 67 | 68 | 69 | 70 |
| 71 | 72 | 73 | 74 | 75 | 76 | 77 | 78 | 79 | 80 |
| 81 | 82 | 83 | 84 | 85 | 86 | 87 | 88 | 89 | 90 |
| 91 | 92 | 93 | 94 | 95 | 96 | 97 | 98 | 99 | 100 |

# On Your Own

**Use the hundred chart to solve.**

**2** There are 24 flowers on a tree. More flowers bloom. Now there are 34 flowers. How many flowers bloom?

_____ flowers

**3** **MP** **Reason** There are 70 flowers on a tree. The wind blows 20 flowers off the tree. How many flowers are on the tree now? Explain your answer.

_____ flowers

| 1 | 2 | 3 | 4 | 5 | 6 | 7 | 8 | 9 | 10 |
|----|----|----|----|----|----|----|----|----|----|
| 11 | 12 | 13 | 14 | 15 | 16 | 17 | 18 | 19 | 20 |
| 21 | 22 | 23 | 24 | 25 | 26 | 27 | 28 | 29 | 30 |
| 31 | 32 | 33 | 34 | 35 | 36 | 37 | 38 | 39 | 40 |
| 41 | 42 | 43 | 44 | 45 | 46 | 47 | 48 | 49 | 50 |
| 51 | 52 | 53 | 54 | 55 | 56 | 57 | 58 | 59 | 60 |
| 61 | 62 | 63 | 64 | 65 | 66 | 67 | 68 | 69 | 70 |
| 71 | 72 | 73 | 74 | 75 | 76 | 77 | 78 | 79 | 80 |
| 81 | 82 | 83 | 84 | 85 | 86 | 87 | 88 | 89 | 90 |
| 91 | 92 | 93 | 94 | 95 | 96 | 97 | 98 | 99 | 100 |

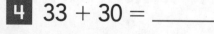

_____

_____

**4** $33 + 30 =$ _____

**5** $80 - 70 =$ _____

**6** $60 - 50 =$ _____

**7** $17 + 40 =$ _____

---

**-÷×** **I'm in a** Learning Mindset!

How did I feel about my learning when I solved Problem 2?

_____

_____

Keep Going **to** Practice and Homework Journal

Name

# Understand and Explain Place Value Addition

( I Can ) use place value to add two-digit numbers.

## Spark Your Learning

How can you represent tens and ones to solve the problem?

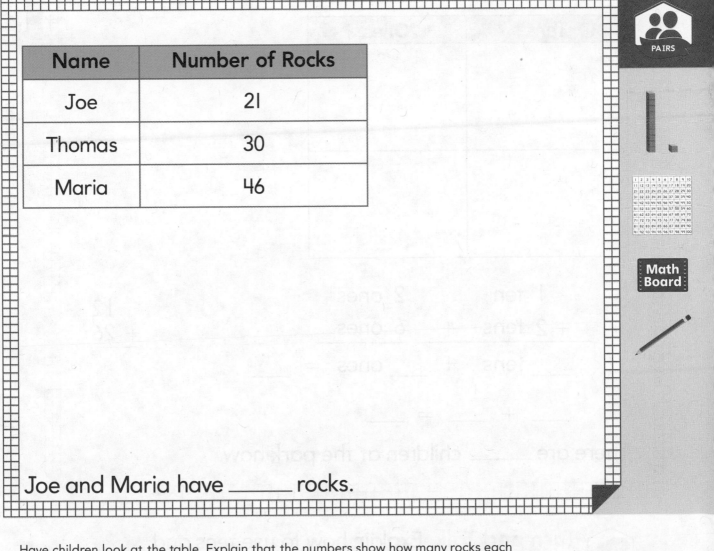

| Name | Number of Rocks |
|--------|-----------------|
| Joe | 21 |
| Thomas | 30 |
| Maria | 46 |

**PAIRS**

**Math Board**

Joe and Maria have _____ rocks.

Have children look at the table. Explain that the numbers show how many rocks each person has in their collection. Read the following: *Joe and Maria put their rock collections together. How many rocks do they have?* Allow children to choose tools to solve the problem. Have them draw to show their work.

# Build Understanding

There are 12 children at the park. Then 26 more children come. How many children are at the park now?

Use tools to solve the problem. How can you use tens and ones to show your work?

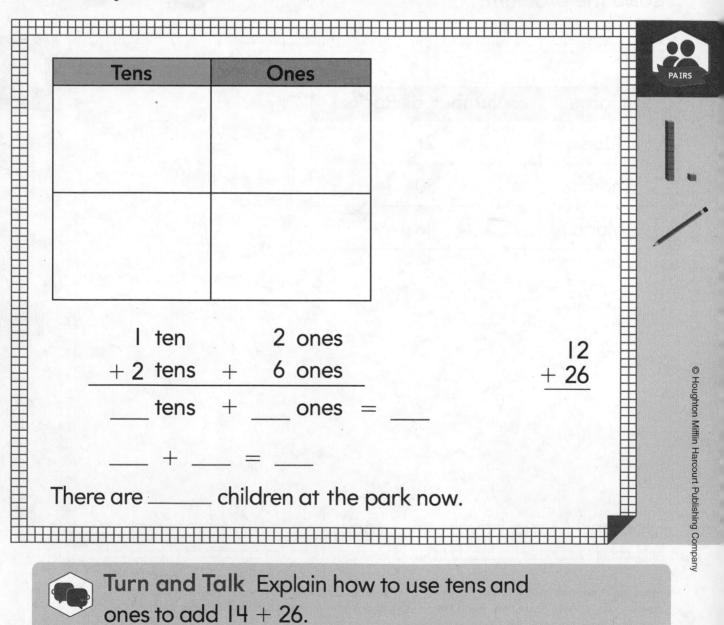

| Tens | Ones |
|------|------|
|      |      |
|      |      |

1 ten        2 ones
+ 2 tens  +  6 ones
___ tens  +  ___ ones  =  ___

___  +  ___  =  ___

$$\begin{array}{r} 12 \\ + 26 \\ \hline \end{array}$$

There are _____ children at the park now.

**Turn and Talk** Explain how to use tens and ones to add 14 + 26.

# Step It Out

**1** ▸ Use tens and ones to add.

**A** Draw tens and ones to show 46.

**THINK:** 4 tens 6 ones

**B** Draw tens and ones to show 28.

**C** Add the tens. Add the ones. Write the equation.

```
  4 tens        6 ones
+ 2 tens      + 8 ones
___ tens  +  ___ ones
```

___ + ___ = ___

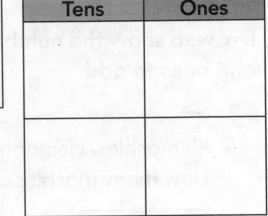

```
   46
 + 28
 ____
```

| Tens | Ones |
|------|------|
|      |      |
|      |      |

**D** Solve.

```
   46
 + 28
 ____
```

..........

# Check Understanding    Math Board

Draw to show the numbers.
Use tens and ones to add.

**1** Stuart has 34 stickers. He gets 42 more.
How many stickers does he have now?          _____ stickers

| Tens | Ones |
|------|------|
|      |      |
|      |      |

```
  3 tens        4 ones
+ 4 tens      + 2 ones
___ tens  +  ___ ones
```

___ + ___ = ___

```
   34
 + 42
 ____
```

# On Your Own

Draw to show the numbers. Use tens and ones to add.

**2** (MP) **Attend to Precision** Dani has 44 marbles. Hector has 31 marbles. How many marbles do they have? _____ marbles

| Tens | Ones |
|------|------|
|      |      |
|      |      |

    4 tens      4 ones
 + 3 tens    + 1 one
_____

   ___ tens + ___ ones

   ___ + ___ = ___

```
  44
+ 31
```

---

**3** Solve 28 + 26.

| Tens | Ones |
|------|------|
|      |      |
|      |      |

    2 tens      8 ones
 + 2 tens    + 6 ones
_____

   ___ tens + ___ ones

   ___ + ___ = ___

```
  28
+ 26
```

---

## I'm in a Learning Mindset!

What can I do to become a better learner?

_____

_____

Name _____

# Understand and Explain Place Value Subtraction

(**I Can**) use place value to subtract tens.

## Spark Your Learning

How can you represent tens to solve the problem?

© Houghton Mifflin Harcourt Publishing Company • Image Credits: ©Valentin Balan/Dreamstine

**PAIRS**

**Math Board**

Equation: _____

Zia has _____ acorns now.

Read the following: *Zia has 50 acorns. She gives 20 to Nate. How many acorns does Zia have now?* Allow children to choose tools. Have children draw to show what they did and write an equation to solve.

# Build Understanding ACTIVITY

Hallie picks 90 apples. She gives away 40 apples. How many apples does she have now?

Use tools to solve the problem. How can you use tens and ones to show your work?

| Tens | Ones |
|------|------|
|      |      |
|      |      |
|      |      |

9 tens     0 ones
− 4 tens   − 0 ones
_____ tens    _____ ones = _____

$$\begin{array}{r} 90 \\ -\ 40 \\ \hline \end{array}$$

Hallie has _____ apples now.

**Turn and Talk** How can you use tens and ones to solve a subtraction problem? Explain the steps you used to subtract 90 − 40.

PAIRS

# Step It Out

**I** Use tens and ones to subtract.

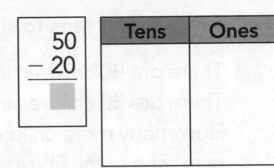

| Tens | Ones |
|------|------|
|      |      |
|      |      |

**A** Draw to show 50.

**THINK:** 5 tens 0 ones

**B** Subtract 20.

**THINK:** Take 2 tens away.

**C** Subtract the tens and ones.

   5 tens       0 ones

−2 tens     −0 ones

_____ tens     _____ ones

**D** Solve.

$$\begin{array}{r} 50 \\ -\ 20 \\ \hline \end{array}$$

# Check Understanding  [Math Board]

**Use tens to subtract.**

**I** Addie has 50 beads. She gives 30 to her friend. How many beads does Addie have now?

_____ beads

| Tens | Ones |
|------|------|
|      |      |
|      |      |
|      |      |

   5 tens       0 ones

−3 tens     −0 ones

_____ tens     _____ ones

$$\begin{array}{r} 50 \\ -\ 30 \\ \hline \end{array}$$

# On Your Own

**MP Reason** Use tens to subtract.

**2** There are 40 children in the gym.
There are 30 children in the library.
How many more children are in the
gym than in the library?

| Tens | Ones |
|------|------|
|      |      |
|      |      |

There are _____ more children in the
gym than in the library.

**3** There are 60 children on a
school bus. Then 10 children get
off the school bus. How can you
find how many children are still on
the school bus? Explain your reasoning.

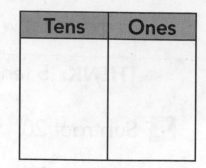

_____

_____

_____

## I'm in a Learning Mindset!

What helps me go from one learning activity to a different one?

_____

_____

Keep Going to Practice and Homework Journal

Name _____

# Solve Two-Digit Addition and Subtraction Problems

( I Can ) choose strategies to solve two-digit addition and subtraction problems.

## Step It Out

**1** A farmer has 90 pumpkins. She sells 40 pumpkins. How many pumpkins are left?

**A** Explain how to solve the problem.

_____

_____

_____

_____

**B** Draw and write to solve.

**THINK:** I can add to subtract.

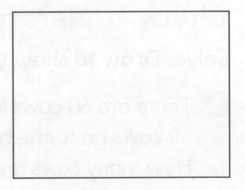

4 tens + _____ tens = 9 tens

So, 9 tens − 4 tens = _____ tens.

90 − 40 = _____

**C** There are _____ pumpkins left.

# Step It Out

**2** Laney has 64 red tulips. She gets 8 more tulips. How many tulips does she have?

**A** Use a strategy to solve. Draw to show your work.

**THINK:** I can make a ten.

**B** Laney has _____ tulips.

>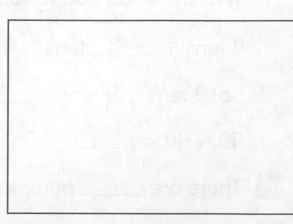
>
> **Turn and Talk** What other strategies could you use to solve this problem? Explain.

## Check Understanding [Math Board]

**Solve. Draw to show your thinking.**

**1** There are 60 cows in a field. 50 cows go to the barn. How many cows are still in the field?

_____ cows

© Houghton Mifflin Harcourt Publishing Company • Image Credits: ©Acik/Adobe Stock

# On Your Own

**Solve.**

**2** Mrs. Kelsie has 32 red apples and 21 green apples. How many apples does she have?

_____ apples

**3** (MP) **Reason** Marco counts 80 pears. He counts 20 fewer peaches than pears. How many peaches does Marco count?

_____ peaches

**4** (MP) **Construct Arguments** Mr. Jones bikes 20 miles to his office. Describe how to find the number of miles he bikes to his office and home again. Solve the problem.

_____

_____

_____

**5** Margo finds 57 orange leaves and 7 red leaves. How many leaves does she find?

_____ leaves

# On Your Own

**Solve. Draw or write to explain.**

**6** Kathy sees 32 orange carrots and 5 purple carrots in the garden. How many carrots does she see?

_____ carrots

**7** **Reason** Sam counts 50 potatoes. Jalen counts 30 potatoes. How many potatoes do Sam and Jalen count together?

_____ potatoes

**8** **Construct Arguments** Mr. Caleb has 30 brown eggs. He has 20 more brown eggs than white eggs. How many white eggs does Mr. Caleb have?

_____ white eggs

Does your answer make sense? Explain.

_____

_____

_____

Name _____

# Practice Facts to 20

( I Can ) solve addition and subtraction facts to 20.

## Step It Out

1 ▶ How many soccer balls and
tennis balls are there?

soccer: 8

football: 7

tennis: 6

baseball: 7

A Look at the sign.

There are _____ soccer balls.

There are _____ tennis balls.

B Think of strategies you can use to add.

**THINK:** I can make a ten.

$8 + 6 =$ 🔲

⟋⟍
_____  _____

$8 +$ _____ $+$ _____

⟋⟍
$10 +$ _____ $=$ _____

C There are _____ soccer balls and
tennis balls.

## Step It Out

**2** There are 12 soccer players on the field. Then 7 players leave the field. How many soccer players are still on the field?

**A** Think of strategies you can use to subtract.

**THINK:** I can add to subtract.

$7 + \underline{\hspace{1cm}} = 12$

So, $12 - 7 = \underline{\hspace{1cm}}$.

**B** \underline{\hspace{1cm}} soccer players are still on the field.

 **Turn and Talk** What other strategy could you use to solve the problem?

## Check Understanding Math Board

Add or subtract to solve.

**1** There are 17 soccer balls and 8 volleyballs. How many more soccer balls are there than volleyballs?

\underline{\hspace{1.5cm}} more soccer balls

# On Your Own

## Add or subtract to solve.

**2** Ava counts 4 small lakes and 7 large lakes on a map. How many lakes does she count altogether?

_____ lakes

**3** **Open Ended** There are 17 rafts in a pool. Riley takes some rafts out of the pool. How many rafts could still be in the pool?

Use an equation to explain.

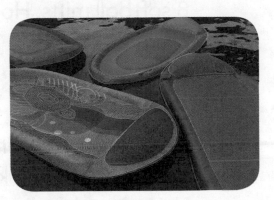

_____

_____

_____

| | | |
|---|---|---|
| **4** $5 + 4 =$ ____ | **5** $8 + 5 =$ ____ | **6** $17 - 9 =$ ____ |
| **7** ____ $= 12 - 3$ | **8** ____ $= 1 + 9$ | **9** ____ $= 11 - 6$ |
| **10** $\begin{array}{r} 14 \\ -\ 8 \\ \hline \end{array}$ | **11** $\begin{array}{r} 5 \\ +\ 7 \\ \hline \end{array}$ | **12** $\begin{array}{r} 3 \\ +\ 3 \\ \hline \end{array}$ |

**MP) Reason** Add or subtract to solve.

**13** There are 12 shirts in a bag. Some are blue and some are red. If 8 shirts are blue, how many of the shirts are red?

_____ red shirts

**14** Coach Jane has 10 baseball mitts and 8 softball mitts. How many mitts does she have?

_____ mitts

**15** There are 14 bowling balls on the rack. 6 balls are taken off the rack. How many bowling balls are on the rack now? Explain.

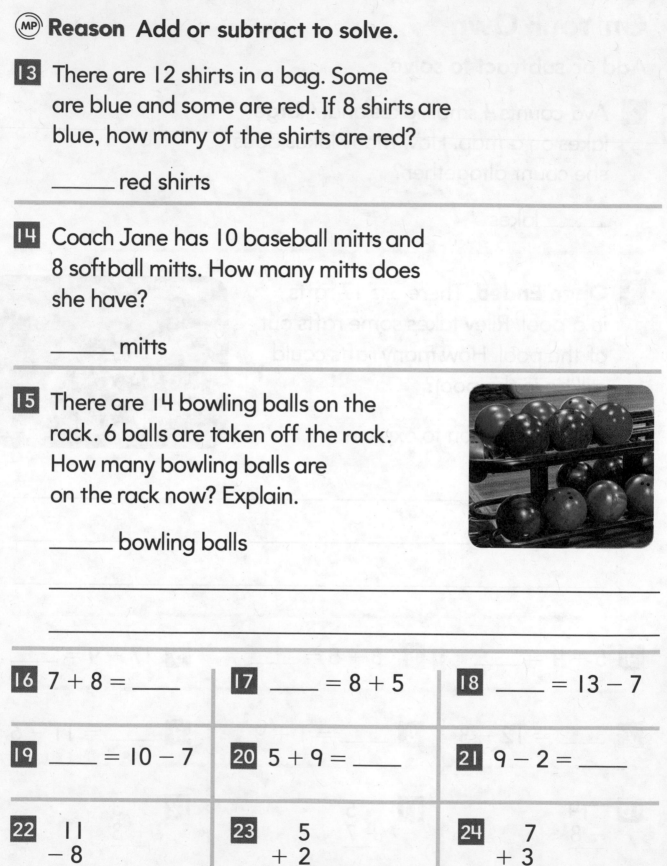

_____ bowling balls

_____

_____

| **16** $7 + 8 =$ _____ | **17** _____ $= 8 + 5$ | **18** _____ $= 13 - 7$ |
|---|---|---|
| **19** _____ $= 10 - 7$ | **20** $5 + 9 =$ _____ | **21** $9 - 2 =$ _____ |
| **22** $\begin{array}{r} 11 \\ -\ 8 \\ \hline \end{array}$ | **23** $\begin{array}{r} 5 \\ +\ 2 \\ \hline \end{array}$ | **24** $\begin{array}{r} 7 \\ +\ 3 \\ \hline \end{array}$ |

Keep Going ▶ Practice and Homework Journal

© Houghton Mifflin Harcourt Publishing Company • Image Credits: ©Mindscape studio/Shutterstock

Name _____

# Practice Two-Digit Addition and Subtraction

( I Can ) add and subtract with two-digit numbers.

## Step It Out

**1** ▶ Mia has a number that is 20 less than the number Tom has. Tom has a number with 3 tens and 0 ones. What number does Mia have?

**A** Start with the number Tom has.

**THINK:** 3 tens 0 ones

The number Tom has is _____.

**B** Find the number Mia has.

**THINK:** The number Mia has is 20 less than the number Tom has.

Equation: _____

**C** The number Mia has is _____.

# Step It Out

**2** Tony and Marci pack box lunches for the class picnic. Tony packs 9 more boxes than Marci. Marci packs 26 boxes. How many boxes does Tony pack?

**A** What information do you need to use?

Marci packs _____ boxes.

Tony packs _____ more boxes than Marci.

**B** Will you add or subtract to solve the problem?

_____

_____

**C** Write an equation. _____

**D** Tony packs _____ boxes.

 **Turn and Talk** What strategy did you use to solve the problem?

# Check Understanding  [Math Board]

**Add or subtract to solve.**

**1** Jason puts 70 carrots on a plate. Friends eat 50 of them. How many carrots are on the plate now?

_____ carrots

# On Your Own

**Add or subtract to solve.**

**2** (MP) **Reason** Lexi makes 24 shapes. Kwesi makes 41 shapes. How many shapes do they make together?

_____ shapes

---

**3** **Open Ended** Ada reads 55 pages of her book. She reads some before lunch and some after lunch. How many pages could she read at each time?

Equation: _____

_____ pages before lunch

_____ pages after lunch

---

**4** _____ $= 41 + 9$

**5** $77 + 8 =$ _____

---

| | | | |
|---|---|---|---|
| **6** $\begin{array}{r} 50 \\ -\ 50 \\ \hline \end{array}$ | **7** $\begin{array}{r} 30 \\ +\ 48 \\ \hline \end{array}$ | **8** $\begin{array}{r} 70 \\ -\ 10 \\ \hline \end{array}$ | **9** $\begin{array}{r} 24 \\ +\ 37 \\ \hline \end{array}$ |
| **10** $\begin{array}{r} 35 \\ +\ 52 \\ \hline \end{array}$ | **11** $\begin{array}{r} 38 \\ +\ 55 \\ \hline \end{array}$ | **12** $\begin{array}{r} 77 \\ +\ 22 \\ \hline \end{array}$ | **13** $\begin{array}{r} 80 \\ -\ 50 \\ \hline \end{array}$ |

# On Your Own

**MP Reason** Add or subtract to solve.

**14** Adam has 7 more stickers than Dan. Dan has 37 stickers. How many stickers does Adam have?

_____ stickers

**15** Mario and Pete each have 40 rocks in their collection. How many rocks do Mario and Pete have?

_____ rocks

**16** Kendra has 50 paper clips. She gives some to Sara. Now Kendra has 20 paper clips. How many does she give to Sara? Does your answer make sense? Explain.

_____ paper clips

_____

_____

**17** _____ $= 30 + 15$

**18** $33 + 25 =$ _____

**19** _____ $= 70 - 40$

**20** $28 + 7 =$ _____

**21** $\begin{array}{r} 41 \\ + 58 \\ \hline \end{array}$

**22** $\begin{array}{r} 60 \\ - 20 \\ \hline \end{array}$

**23** $\begin{array}{r} 22 \\ + 63 \\ \hline \end{array}$

**24** $\begin{array}{r} 43 \\ + 16 \\ \hline \end{array}$

Keep Going ▶ Practice and Homework Journal

# Review

## Concepts and Skills

### Add or subtract to solve.

**1** 40 + 25 = _____   **2** 50 − 30 = _____

**3** 20 + 46 = _____   **4** 90 − 50 = _____

**5**　　65
　　　+ 22
　　　_____

**6**　　40
　　　+ 49
　　　_____

**7**　　80
　　　− 30
　　　_____

**8**　　53
　　　+ 38
　　　_____

### Fill in the bubble next to the correct answer.

**9** Kaya has 58 red buttons and 8 blue buttons.
How many buttons does she have?

○ 66 buttons　　○ 57 buttons　　○ 56 buttons

**10** There are 12 jars of peanuts on a shelf.
Mr. Grace buys 3 of them. How many jars
of peanuts are on the shelf now?

○ 11 jars　　○ 10 jars　　○ 9 jars

**Fill in the bubble next to the correct answer.**

**11** Delaney has 80 marbles. She gives 20 marbles to her friend. How many marbles does Delaney have now?

○ 90 marbles      ○ 70 marbles      ○ 60 marbles

**12** Sara swims 24 laps. Then she swims 25 more laps. How many laps does she swim?

○ 49 laps      ○ 43 laps      ○ 37 laps

---

**Use the hundred chart to solve.**

**13** Beth counts 54 peaches.
Don counts some peaches.
They count 74 peaches in all.
How many peaches does
Don count?

_____ peaches

| 1 | 2 | 3 | 4 | 5 | 6 | 7 | 8 | 9 | 10 |
|---|---|---|---|---|---|---|---|---|---|
| 11 | 12 | 13 | 14 | 15 | 16 | 17 | 18 | 19 | 20 |
| 21 | 22 | 23 | 24 | 25 | 26 | 27 | 28 | 29 | 30 |
| 31 | 32 | 33 | 34 | 35 | 36 | 37 | 38 | 39 | 40 |
| 41 | 42 | 43 | 44 | 45 | 46 | 47 | 48 | 49 | 50 |
| 51 | 52 | 53 | 54 | 55 | 56 | 57 | 58 | 59 | 60 |
| 61 | 62 | 63 | 64 | 65 | 66 | 67 | 68 | 69 | 70 |
| 71 | 72 | 73 | 74 | 75 | 76 | 77 | 78 | 79 | 80 |
| 81 | 82 | 83 | 84 | 85 | 86 | 87 | 88 | 89 | 90 |
| 91 | 92 | 93 | 94 | 95 | 96 | 97 | 98 | 99 | 100 |

---

**Add or subtract.**

**14** $16 - 7 =$ _____

**15** $8 + 5 =$ _____

**16** $6 + 9 =$ _____

**17** $14 - 8 =$ _____